Paint your own

Owls

TOP THAT

Top That Publishing
Tide Mill Way, Woodbridge, Suffolk, IP12 1AP, UK
www.imaginethat.com
Top That is an imprint of Imagine That Group Ltd
Copyright © 2018 Imagine That Group Ltd

Hoo-hoo!

If you like owls then this is the kit for you! It's packed with incredible and outrageous owl facts and includes everything you need to paint four cute owls of your own. It's going to be a hoot!

Owl Fact:

Owls don't just hoot, they also whistle, growl, purr, and even hiss!

Big Owl
Project

About Big Owl

When anyone in the wood
has a problem or needs help they
go and talk to Big Owl. No matter how
difficult the problem, Big Owl can usually
solve it. Everyone knows owls are very wise
and Big Owl is the oldest
and wisest owl
in the whole
wood.

Owl Fact:

The great gray owl
is the longest owl at
up to 33 in. long!

Color Palette

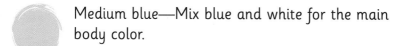

Medium blue—Mix blue and white for the main body color.

Light blue—Mix white and a little blue for the zigzag belly detail.

Light green—Mix yellow and a little green for the striped wing and eye details.

Orange—Mix yellow and a little red for the beak and feet.

Straight from the pot:
Use the black paint for Big Owl's pupils and the green for the main wing and outer eye color.

Top Tip

Take your time when painting the stripe and zigzag details. Try to space them evenly for the best results.

Cleaning Up

Owls preen their feathers
every day to keep them clean
and in great condition. They do this
when they wake up, often for several hours!
Super-clean feathers mean healthy owls,
great flight, and
good hunting!

Owl Fact:

Owls can find it
difficult to keep warm.
They have lots and lots
of downy feathers to keep their body heat in.

Meet the Family

Owls can lay up to 12 eggs,
but they usually lay three to four.
When the babies, called owlets, hatch
out, they only have a thin coat of down.
By the time they are two weeks old,
a warmer and heavier second coat of
down appears. Cozy!

Owl Fact:

Owlets are fed
as many as ten
times a day by
their dad. That's
a lot of meals!

Curious
Owl
Project

About Curious Owl

Meet Curious Owl. She spends most of the day tucked up safely in a tree hollow, but when the light begins to fade she is out exploring. All owls are clever and inquisitive, and Curious Owl is no exception. With great long-distance vision and powerful hearing, Curious Owl knows everything going on in the wood.

Owl Fact:

Owls cannot move or "roll" their eyes like humans. Instead they can move their whole head, almost 270 degrees!

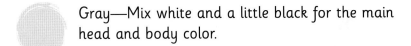

Color Palette

Gray—Mix white and a little black for the main head and body color.

Light pink—Mix white and a little red for the heart and wings.

Dark pink—Mix red and some white to add the feather detail to the heart.

Orange—Mix yellow and a little red for the beak and feet.

Straight from the pot: Use the black paint for Curious Owl's pupils.

Top Tip

Use a toothpick to add a white dotted pattern over the body and head.

Home Sweet Home

Many owls nest in holes in trees, but some kinds live in old hawk or squirrel nests, or even in old mammal burrows! Wherever they nest, it is important that they are close to their territory, where they hunt.

Owl Fact:

Some farmers provide special nesting sites for owls, to encourage the birds to hunt down rodents on the farm. Smart move!

Hide-and-go-seek

Owls are shy birds. You can sometimes hear them, but they can be quite difficult to spot, especially as they mostly come out at night! Their coloring helps them to blend into their surroundings and can change from season to season. Clever!

Owl Fact:

An owl's feathers are completely replaced by new ones once a year. This is called molting and it takes about three months.

Wise Owls

Owls are thought to be among the smartest of all birds. They have been a cultural symbol for thousands of years. Images of owls have been found in cave paintings and in Egyptian pictures and symbols.

Owl Fact:

Fossil remains show that owls were already around 60 million years ago!

Eye-eye!

Owls have excellent eyesight, which helps them to be amazing hunters. Their super-big eyes also have three eyelids! One is for blinking, another is for sleeping, and a third is for keeping the eye clean.

Owl Fact:

An owl's eyesight is 100 times better in dim light than a human's!

Crafty
Owl
Project

About Crafty Owl

Crafty Owl is a master of surprise! The other woodland animals often get a shock when they turn around and see Crafty Owl standing behind them. Owls like Crafty Owl fly so quietly because their big wings mean they can float through the air. They also have special feathers which reduce the noise they make when they fly.

Owl Fact:

Owls can fly almost silently, which is how they sneak up on prey like voles and mice!

Color Palette

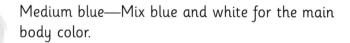

Medium blue—Mix blue and white for the main body color.

Light blue—Mix white and a little blue for the belly and around the eyes.

Light green—Mix yellow and a little green for the model base.

Pink—Mix red and white for the wings.

Straight from the pot:
Use the black paint for
Crafty Owl's pupils and the yellow
paint for the beak and feet.

Top Tip

Once the wings are dry,
mix white and a little
red for a lighter pink, then
add the heart details
using a toothpick.

Get a Grip!

An owl's talons are massive, sharp, and curved—ideal for catching prey. They do the work once the owl's eyes and ears have spotted its next meal! Run mouse, run!

Owl Fact:

Owls have been known to attack humans when they feel threatened, especially when they have eggs or young to protect.

How Many?

There are around 200
different species of owl, but
there are only two main groups—
"typical owls" and "barn owls." They
live in all regions of the world, except in
Antarctica and a few far-away islands.

Owl Fact:

A group of owls is
called a "parliament."
A parliament of owls
features in the
Narnia Chronicles by
C.S. Lewis.

Crazy Owl
Project

About Crazy Owl

The wackiest owl in the wood,
Crazy Owl is always getting up
to mischief. Just when most of
the forest animals are going to bed,
Crazy Owl wakes up and starts having fun.
With her noisy squawks and hoots, and her
nosy nature, Crazy Owl is always getting
her beak into trouble!

Owl Fact:

Owls are nocturnal,
which means they are
active at night. Their
large eyes help them
to see in the dark.

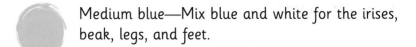

Color Palette

Medium blue—Mix blue and white for the irises, beak, legs, and feet.

Pink—Mix white and a little red for the outer eye details.

Light green—Mix yellow and a little green for the belly.

Brown—Mix green and red for the model base.

Straight from the pot:
Use the black paint for Crazy Owl's pupils and yellow for the body and wings.

Top Tip

Once the green belly area is dry, paint blue, pink, and yellow dots using a toothpick for zany added detail!

Face Facts!

Owls have a flat, disk-shaped face that funnels the sounds made by their prey to their ears. The sounds are magnified by as much as ten times, so a hungry owl can find prey in almost total darkness.

Owl Fact:

You can recognize a barn owl from its heart-shaped face. Cute!

Out in the Cold

Snowy owls are the only owls that have all-over white coloring. The females also have gray and black speckles. All this makes the perfect camouflage for their habitat in the cold, snowy Arctic.

Owl Fact:

Snowy owls can eat more than 1,600 lemmings (Arctic rodents) a year. Gulp!